THIS BOOK BELONGS TO

GARFIELD'S No.1 FAN –

NAME ....

AGE ....

ADDRESS ....

....

....

TELEPHONE No. ....

DATE ....

Hello to our friends in the U.K.!

Garfield and I are pleased to present the first ever Garfield Annual. It's filled with strips, stories, puzzles, and the one thing Garfield loves more than anything in the world – namely, Garfield!

Not long ago Garfield and I visited the United Kingdom. Garfield thought the Tower of London would be a great place to keep Odie. We played golf at St. Andrew's, and Garfield got two birdies. (Fortunately, they both escaped.)

Garfield and I both appreciate the love and support we receive from loyal Garfield readers like you. Hope you enjoy your Garfield Annual!

Best wishes from
Garfield and myself,

JIM DAVIS

THE
1990
GARFIELD
ANNUAL
Based on the characters
created by
JIM DAVIS
Written by
Gordon Volke
RAVETTE BOOKS

CONTENTS

Published by Ravette Books Limited 1989.

Printed and bound for Ravette Books Limited, 3 Glenside Estate, Star Road, Partridge Green, Horsham, West Sussex RH13 8RA
by BPCC Paulton Books Limited

ISBN 1 85304 159 9

A GIANT STEP FOR GARFIELD

"I'm bored, Pooky!" sighed Garfield. "Bored, bored, bored!" Garfield and his beloved teddy were sitting on the sofa. It was a hot, July afternoon and everyone was out. Jon had gone to play golf. Odie was chasing butterflies in the garden. And Arlene had gone to visit her mother.

Idly, Garfield switched on the television. As the picture swam into focus, Garfield saw a spaceman stepping out of his spaceship. "Look, Pooky!" he cried excitedly, "A space film." But nothing very exciting happened. No aliens appeared firing ray-guns. The spaceman just hopped about a bit and then stuck a flag in the ground. Suddenly, Garfield understood. "That Neil Armstrong!" he exclaimed. "The first man on the moon!"

"Twenty years ago today," said the voice of the TV announcer, "man first set foot on the surface of the moon." Garfield closed his eyes. "I wish I could be the first **cat** on the moon," he sighed, "then Jon would stop nagging me about being fat and lazy." Garfield gave Pooky an excited cuddle and imagined himself in a spacesuit, planting a flag on the moon. "This is just one small paw-print for me," said Astrocat Garfield, "but a giant paw-print for the feline-kind."

Leaving Pooky on the sofa, Garfield got up and wandered round the house. "Of course there's no way I can really go into space," he thought, sadly. Then Garfield remembered Jon's computer. "There's a space-game on that!" cried Garfield, gleefully, "at least I can **pretend** to be landing on the moon."

Garfield turned on the computer. It made a bleeping noise that sounded just like the astronauts on the moon. Then a message flashed up on the screen. "On this very special day," it said, "your dreams can come true. Press key 'T' for 'thought'!" Breathlessly, Garfield obeyed. The computer told him that it had the power to grant one wish. All Garfield had to do was to think about what he wanted and it would come true. "I'd like a little space rocket to take me to the moon," thought Garfield.

Garfield pressed the 'T' key and waited. Nothing seemed to happen. Then Odie could be heard barking frantically outside. Hurrying into the garden, Garfield found a spaceship with his name on it waiting on the lawn. "It's worked!" he gasped. "My wish **has** come true!"

Garfield jumped into the rocket and pressed the controls. VROOM!

The little craft shot up into the air. "'Bye, Odie. 'Bye, Pooky," called Garfield, as Jon's house became smaller and smaller below him. Soon, Garfield was cruising through space, on course for the moon.

The moon came into view. It rushed at Garfield, growing larger by the second. "Stand by for touch-down," murmured Garfield, in his best astronaut's voice. WHOOSH! The landing-gear extended and Garfield's craft settled on the surface like a giant fly. Garfield opened the hatch and jumped out.

"Time for a moon-walk," thought Garfield. "I might even try some of those funny moon-hops. I like the idea of travelling several metres in one hop." However, when our hero tried to lift his feet, he found he was stuck! The surface of the moon was all sticky. And when he removed his space helmet, he noticed a familiar smell. "Cheese!" he cried. "The moon **is** made of cheese!"

Garfield bent down and had a taste. It was definitely true. He was standing on a layer of soft, melted cheese. Digging a little deeper with his paw, Garfield made another astonishing discovery. Beneath the cheese was a layer of soft, white stuff. "It can't be!" thought Garfield. But it was! "Pasta!" gasped Garfield. "Underneath the cheese is a layer of pasta." Garfield hardly needed to dig any deeper to discover what lay under the pasta.

"Meat sauce!" he giggled, as the delicious liquid came bubbling up through the hole he had made. Now Garfield understood everything."The moon isn't made of cheese," he whispered. "It's made of LASAGNE!"

Garfield sat down and ate his fill. Then he ate his fill again. "If I carry on at this rate," he chuckled, "I'll make a crater they can see from Earth." After this delicious feast, Garfield felt very happy. "I'm going to stay here for the rest of my life," he announced.

Half-an-hour later, Garfield was not so sure. After all that lasagne, he wanted a nap in his cosy little bed. Every time he tried to lie down here, he got a face full of sticky cheese. Then Garfield began to miss his friends."Jon would just be coming back from golf now," thought Garfield. "He'd be making a fuss of me and telling me how well he played." Suddenly, Garfield remembered he had a date with Arlene that night. "She'll be really mad with me if I don't turn up." he spluttered. And Garfield missed Odie. "I never thought I'd say it," sobbed the homesick puss, "but I wish I could see my old pal bounding towards me right now in a silly-looking spacesuit!"

That was it! Garfield decided to head for home. With a last look round at the acres of lasagne he no longer wanted, Garfield made his way back to the spaceship. It took a long time because of the sticky cheese, but he made it in the end. "Fire rocket motor!" he commanded. Click! (Nothing!) Click! (Nothing!) "Even Jon's old car starts better than this!" grumbled Garfield. Then he looked at the fuel gauge. It showed EMPTY! "I only asked the computer for a spaceship **to** the moon!" wailed Garfield. "I didn't say anything about getting back!!"

Astrocat Garfield seemed stranded in space. But help was at hand. Shooting stars kept whizzing overhead. Using the ejector-seat from his spacerocket, Garfield managed to propel himself into the air. PLOP! He timed it perfectly and landed on a passing star. "Home, James!" he cried.

Garfield held tight as the glittering star sped through the endless blackness towards the Earth. "I hope I'm all right re-entering the Earth's atmosphere," thought Garfield. "I believe the friction makes everything very hot."

Sure enough, as the Earth drew closer and Garfield was able to make out the familiar shape of the continents, it did begin to grow warmer. Soon, Garfield was sweating. "I'm not going to be able to stand this!" he spluttered. "After all, I am wearing a fur coat." Garfield rocked from side to side in an attempt to escape from the searing heat. Then there was a sudden, painful bump! Garfield had landed!

Garfield opened his eyes and looked around. Yes, he was back home all right. Surely he should have more than an aching back after hitting the ground at supersonic speed. Suddenly, Garfield understood. He had only fallen out of bed! "I had a nap attack!" he chortled. "My space adventure was all a dream."

Garfield ran 'round the house and burst in the front door. Jon had left Pooky and a pan of freshly-baked lasagne waiting to welcome him. Garfield picked up Pooky and gave him a cuddle. "It's great to be back!" he told his little pal.

STAR PORTRAIT
GARFIELD AND POOKY

GARFIELD
OOOO! A WARM SPOT
IT'S NO SUNBEAM, BUT IT WILL DO
© 1986 United Feature Syndicate, Inc.
ROWRR!
THE FIRST RULE OF OWNING A CAT: "LOOK BEFORE YOU SIT"
JIM DAVIS

I'M GOING TO GIVE GARFIELD A LITTLE TREAT TODAY
GARFIELD
ARRRGH!
GARFIELD
© 1986 United Feature Syndicate, Inc.
YOU DON'T LIKE SHAVED COCONUT?
SHAVED COCONUT, YES. ALBINO SPIDERS, NO
GARFIELD
JIM DAVIS
CATS HAVE AN INCREDIBLE INNATE ABILITY TO SENSE WHEN YOU ARE FEELING BLUE
© 1986 United Feature Syndicate, Inc.
JON, I SENSE YOU ARE FEELING BLUE
SEE?
BONK!
CHEER UP!
JIM DAVIS
WE HAVE HERE THE LAST PIECE OF CAKE, GARFIELD
JIM DAVIS
I SUGGEST WE DRAW STRAWS TO SEE WHO GETS IT
© 1986 United Feature Syndicate, Inc.
I'M NOT A BETTING MAN
AND NOW THE WORLD-CLASS PANCAKE FLIPPER WILL DEMONSTRATE HIS SKILL
JIM DAVIS
© 1986 United Feature Syndicate, Inc.
PARDON MY IGNORANCE, MR. WORLD-CLASS PANCAKE FLIPPER, BUT SHOULDN'T THE STOVE BE TURNED ON FIRST?

JIM DAVIS
BONE BREATH!
© 1982 United Feature Syndicate, Inc.
JIM DAVIS
© 1982 United Feature Syndicate, Inc.
TOO MUCH ROPE
JIM DAVIS
© 1982 United Feature Syndicate, Inc.
DON'T YOU DARE WALK ACROSS THE TABLE WITH THOSE MUDDY FEET
JIM DAVIS
© 1982 United Feature Syndicate, Inc.
I MUST HAVE BLOWN A FUSE

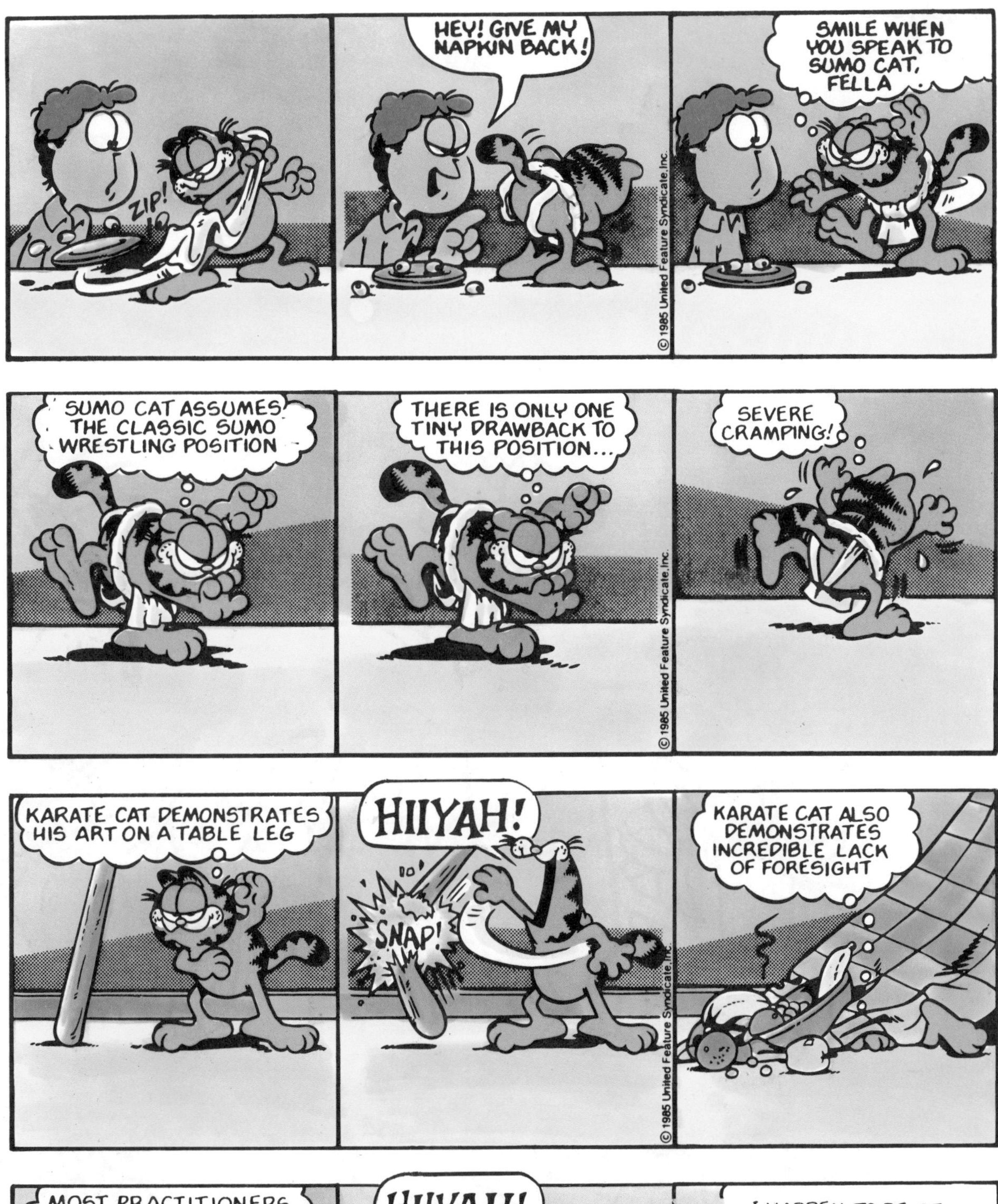
ZIP!
HEY! GIVE MY NAPKIN BACK!
SMILE WHEN YOU SPEAK TO SUMO CAT, FELLA
© 1985 United Feature Syndicate, Inc.
SUMO CAT ASSUMES THE CLASSIC SUMO WRESTLING POSITION
THERE IS ONLY ONE TINY DRAWBACK TO THIS POSITION...
SEVERE CRAMPING!
© 1985 United Feature Syndicate, Inc.
KARATE CAT DEMONSTRATES HIS ART ON A TABLE LEG
HIIYAH!
SNAP!
KARATE CAT ALSO DEMONSTRATES INCREDIBLE LACK OF FORESIGHT
© 1985 United Feature Syndicate, Inc.

MOST PRACTITIONERS OF KARATE ARE IMPERVIOUS TO PAIN
JIM DAVIS
HIIYAH!
SMACK!
I HAPPEN TO BE OF THE PERVIOUS TO PAIN PERSUASION
© 1985 United Feature Syndicate, Inc.

The joy is in the giving ...

out the fun is in the getting!

AMAZIN

The world's heaviest cat was a ten-year-old tabby named 'Himmy' who lived in Queensland, Australia. On the day he died, March 12th 1986, he weighed a colossal 21.3 kilograms (46 lb, 15¼ oz). That's about the weight of an average 5-year-old child!

Hey, Guinness Book!
Get a load of this!

The smallest cat in the world is a male Siamese cross called 'Ebony-Eb-Honey Cat' from Idaho, USA. In February 1984, at the age of nearly 2 years old, this tiny ball of fluff only weighed 0.79 kilograms, (1 lb 12 oz). That's much less than a normal bag of sugar from the supermarket.

Nermal needs to
eat more lasagne!

One way to reach a ripe old age
is to make sure you get plenty
of sleep. So I should
live to be 100 . . . !

The oldest cat on record was owned by Mrs. T. Holway from Devon. On November 28th, 1939, her male tabby called 'Puss' celebrated his 36th birthday. That means he lived almost from the time of Queen Victoria to the outbreak of the Second World War. (The following day, Puss died!)

CAT FACTS

Fully-grown female cats are known as 'queens' and some of them have produced more offspring than our entire Royal Family put together!

The largest litter of kittens ever recorded was delivered by operation to a queen called 'Tarawood Antigone', owned by Mrs. Valerie Gane of Oxfordshire. On August 7, 1970, the 4-year-old Burmese gave birth to a total of 19 kittens! Of the 15 survivors, all were male except for one!

The largest litter of kittens that all survived was produced by a cat called 'Bluebell'. This Persian Blue, owned by Mrs. Elenore Dawson of Cape Province, South Africa, delivered 14 healthy kittens in December 1974.

The title of feline 'supermum' of all time must be awarded to 'Dusty' from Bonham in Texas, USA. Born in 1935, the queen had given birth to an incredible 420 kittens by the time she had her last litter (a single kitten) on June 12, 1952. That's about 25 kittens every year!

Another 'top cat' is the kitten belonging to Josephine Aufdenblatten of Geneva, Switzerland, who at the age of only four months followed a party of climbers up the Matterhorn mountain in the Alps. On September 6, 1950, this 'Chris Bonnington of the cat world' joined the climbers on the summit, some 4,478 metres (14,691 feet) above sea-level!

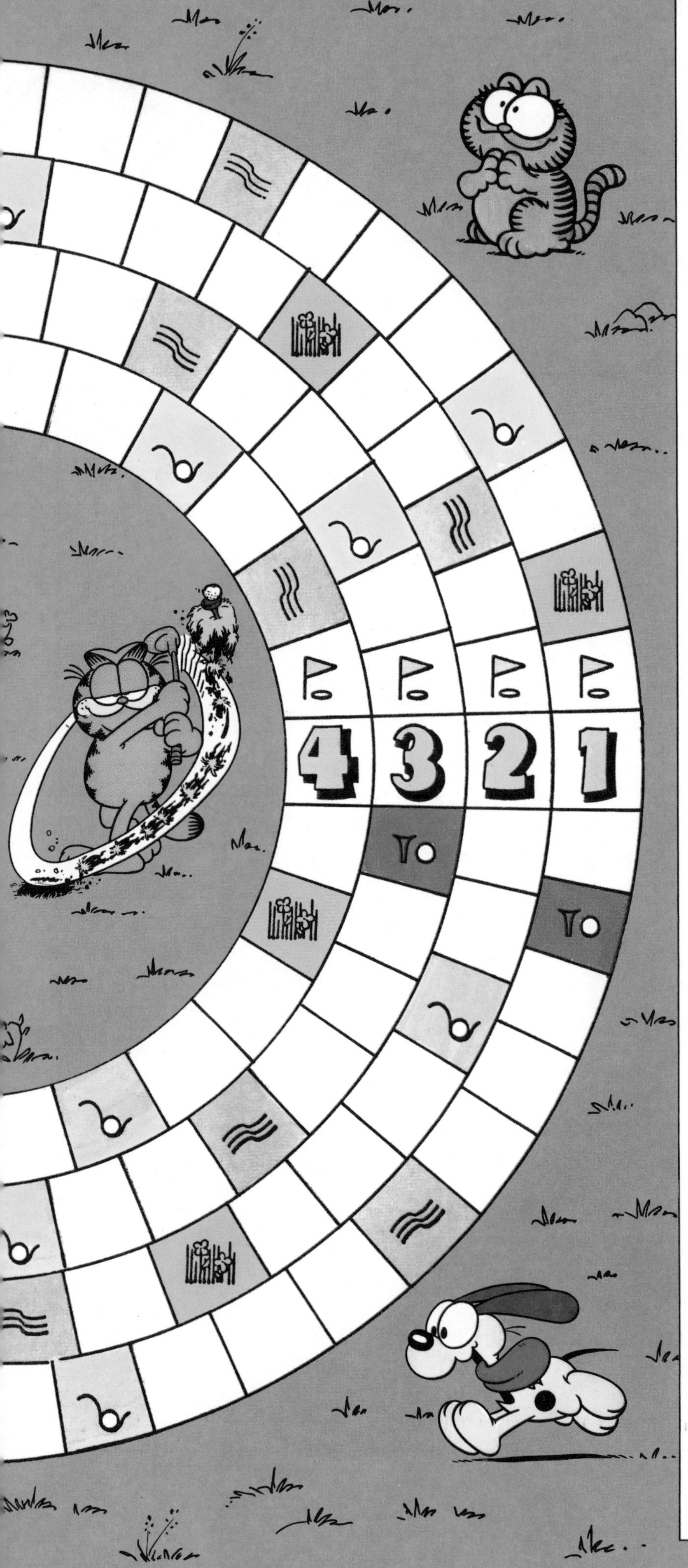

GARFIELD – TO THE 'FORE'

Garfield was tired of being left alone while Jon went to play golf. So the sporting puss decided to try a round himself. Odie, Nermal, and Arlene went along to watch. Why don't YOU join in the fun too?

Garfield's Golf Game is easy to play. All you need is a die and four different coloured counters. These can come from another game (such as tiddly-winks), or you can use old buttons. The game is best with four players.

To start, each player places his counter on Number 1 of the appropriate colour. (Red counter on red Number 1 and so on). This means each player is on a different track. Once the player throws a six, he can begin to move forward round his track in a clockwise direction. Obstacles like bunkers and high grass are in the way. The problems they pose are explained in the box below. Once a player has been right round the track, he must throw the dice until it shows exactly the right number to reach the hole. When this is achieved, the player has completed one hole.

There are four holes on Garfield's golf course, so the player who has successfully been round the board once moves over to the next track and begins all over again. The winner is the first player who completes all four circuits of the board.

Explanation of the symbols

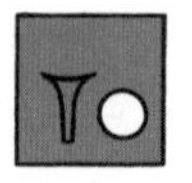

Missed the ball! Go back to the beginning of this track.

Water ditch. Advance two squares to avoid it.

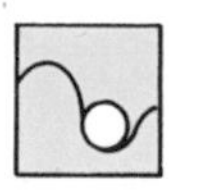

Bunker! You need another stroke to get out. Throw dice again.

Long grass. You have to find your lost ball. Miss one go.

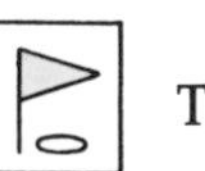

The hole.

GARFIELD
DINNER TIME, GARFIELD!
I RAN OUT OF CANNED CAT FOOD.
I'M SURE YOU KNOW WHAT TO DO WITH THIS DRIED STUFF
GARFIELD
JIM DAVIS
I CERTAINLY DO
GARFIELD
© 1985 United Feature Syndicate, Inc.
GARFIELD
WOAAAH!
ENJOYING YOUR CAT FOOD, GARFIELD?
WE MUST HAVE IT MORE OFTEN
GARFIELD

OKAY, ODIE, YOU PUSH THE CAKE OFF AND I'LL CATCH IT
JIM DAVIS

DON'T TIP IT! DON'T TIP IT!
© 1982 United Feature Syndicate, Inc.
YOU TIPPED IT

PUNT
JIM DAVIS

HAVE YOU KICKED YOUR DOG TODAY?
© 1982 United Feature Syndicate, Inc.

JIM DAVIS

© 1982 United Feature Syndicate, Inc.

Z
JIM DAVIS 3-16

© 1982 United Feature Syndicate, Inc.
Z

MMMPH FMOPH FWEEF
THAT IS CORRECT. IT IS TIME TO GET UP

FOLD
FOLD
CAN I PLAY TOO?
SURE... GRAB HOLD
© 1981 United Feature Syndicate, Inc.
SLEEP ON MY TEDDY BEAR. WILL YOU?!
Z
JIM DAVIS
Z
I WISH I COULD DO THAT
Z
© 1981 United Feature Syndicate, Inc.
GARFIELD, I GET THE IMPRESSION YOU DON'T LIKE NERMAL
NONSENSE. I LOVE NERMAL
I JUST LOOOVE NERMAL!
UH...UH, GARFIELD
© 1981 United Feature Syndicate, Inc.
HEY, NERMAL, WANNA RACE TO THE FRONT DOOR?
YOU WIN
SLAM
© 1981 United Feature Syndicate, Inc.

I WONDER HOW FAST I CAN RUN
JIM DAVIS
I WONDER WHAT WOULD HAPPEN IF I HIT THIS KITTY DOOR AT MACH 2
© 1984 United Feature Syndicate, Inc.
I WONDER IF KILLING A MAILMAN IS A FEDERAL OFFENSE

COME ON, MAILMAN, DELIVER THAT MAIL
AND WHEN YOU DO, I'M GOING TO LEAP ON YOU AND ALL THAT WILL BE LEFT WILL BE YOUR MAILBAG AND THAT SILLY-LOOKING HAT OF YOURS
© 1984 United Feature Syndicate, Inc.
HAS THE MAILMAN COME YET, GARFIELD?
NO, HE'S STILL STANDING AT THE END OF THE SIDEWALK SOBBING

WHAMM
RATS! I MISSED HIM
© 1984 United Feature Syndicate, Inc.
APPARENTLY, NO ONE EVER TOLD HIM TO LOOK BOTH WAYS BEFORE CROSSING THE STREET
SCREECH

BE A GOOD BOY AND FETCH THE MAIL, GARFIELD
OUI, MON CAPITAINE
ROWR
CLOBBER
© 1984 United Feature Syndicate, Inc.
DID YOU HURT HIM BAD?
OH, JUST A FEW LACERATIONS, ABRASIONS AND INTERNAL INJURIES. I WAS IN A GOOD MOOD

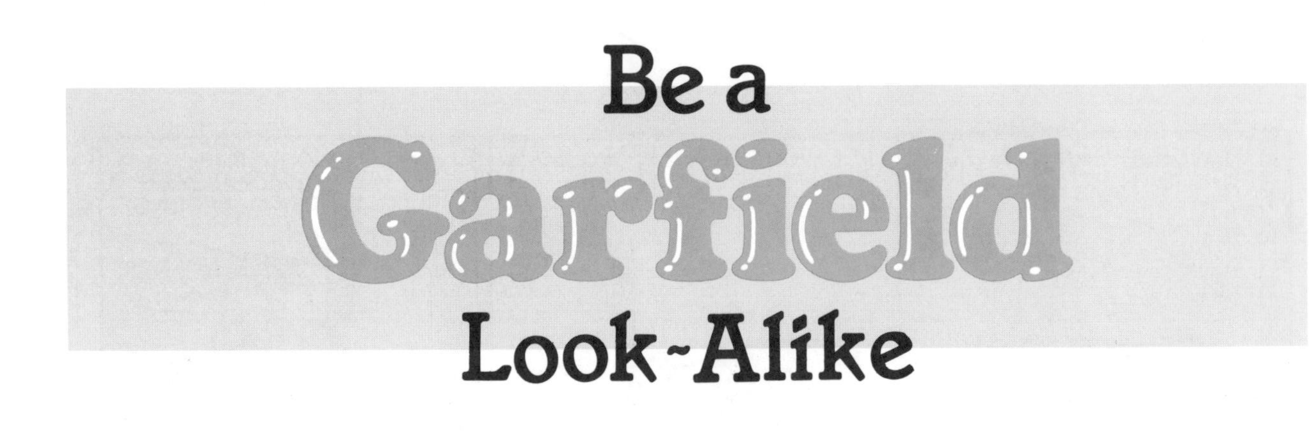

Be a Garfield Look-Alike

Here's your chance to look like Garfield! This Garfield mask is quick and easy to make. All you have to do is to cut round the dotted line and fix a piece of string or elastic between the two black dots to keep the mask in place. To make your Garfield mask stronger, you can stick it onto some thin cardboard first.

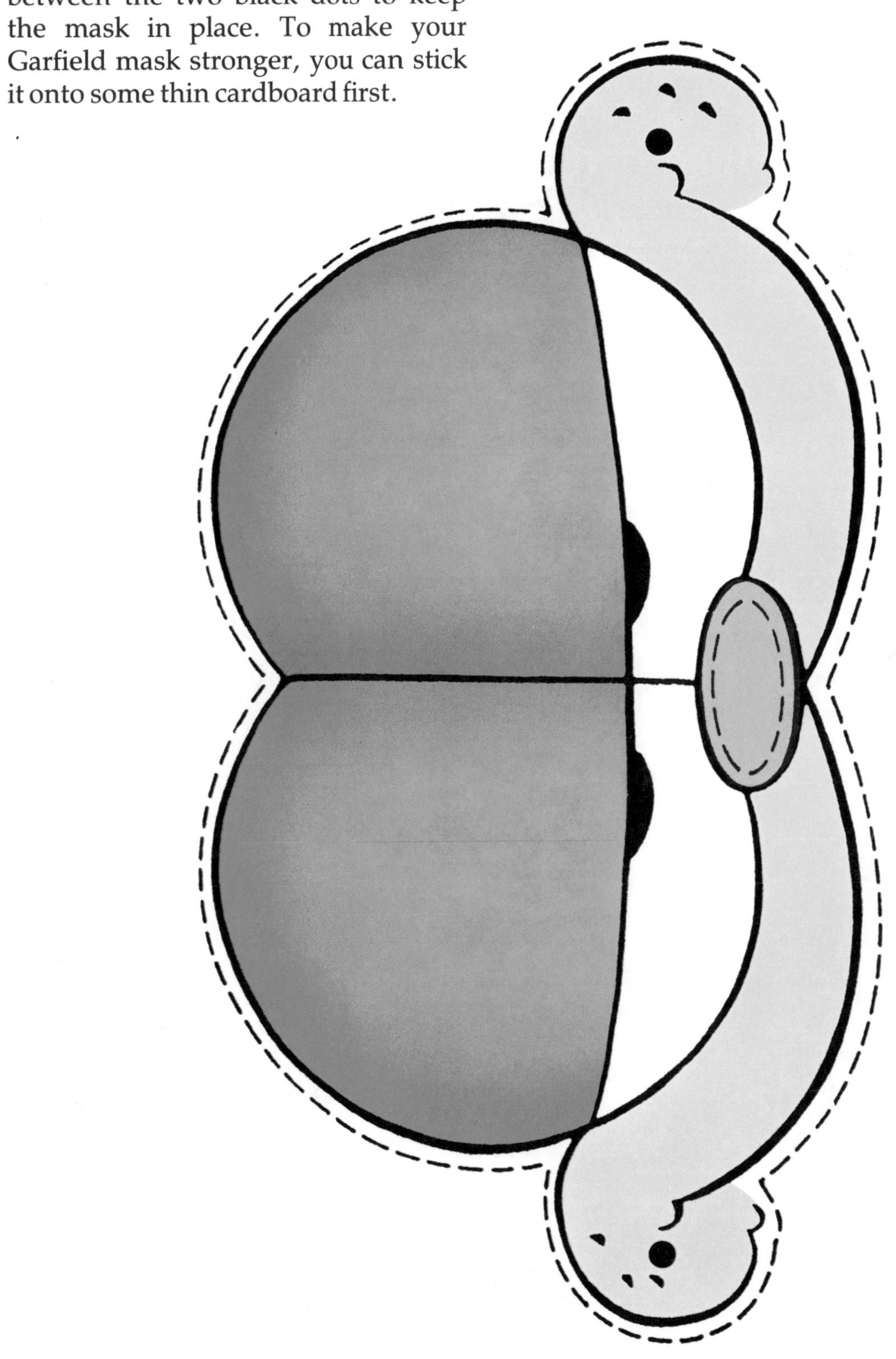

STAR PORTRAIT
JON

SIMPLE LASAGNE

Everyone knows that lasagne is Garfield's favourite dish. So here's a simple way to make it. First of all, though, a warning. Young children should not attempt to make this dish without a parent or a grown-up present. All children should ask their parents' permission to use the kitchen.

Lasagne is made of three separate elements, placed on top of one another and then baked. These elements are: a bolognaise sauce, a cheese sauce and the pasta. The following recipe tells you the easiest and most straightforward way to make all three.

THE BOLOGNAISE SAUCE

450g/1lb of minced beef or soya.
225g/8oz tin of tomatoes.
100g/4oz tube of tomato puree.
Pinch of salt, pepper, mixed herbs and sugar.
1 onion.
Cooking oil.
Garlic (single clove of fresh garlic or pinch of garlic powder).
Water.

Put a small amount of cooking oil into the saucepan and heat gently. Chop the onion and fry slowly until it softens. Add the mince and stir slowly until it changes from red to grey. Add the tin of tomatoes, including the juice, and stir in. Add the whole tube of tomato puree and a little water to make the mixture more liquid. Add the salt, pepper, mixed herbs, sugar and garlic (omitting any you don't like!) Simmer gently for about 10 minutes and allow to cool down.

THE CHEESE SAUCE

100g/4oz of butter.
Self-raising flour.
40cl/¾ pint of milk.
225/8oz of mature cheddar cheese.

Put the butter into another saucepan and heat very gently until it melts. Stir in enough flour to make a thick, sticky paste. Turn up the heat and stir vigorously as you add the milk. Keep stirring until all the lumps dissolve and turn the heat down again when you have a smooth, creamy white sauce. (Making this roux is the tricky bit. You may not get it right first time!) Cut the cheese into lumps and add to the mixture, stirring continuously until the cheese has melted. Leave to cool.

THE PASTA

There are two types of pasta you can use to make lasagne. Egg lasagne is a yellow colour and is made from durum wheat and egg. Lasagne verdi is green and is made from durum wheat and spinach. Both are equally tasty.

There is also a choice between traditional lasagne that you have to boil and oven-ready lasagne that can be used straight from the packet. Traditional lasagne is getting increasingly difficult to come by these days and is very awkward to cook because the sheets tend to stick together, so for the purposes of this recipe let's assume you are using the 'quick-cook' lasagne which is available in most supermarkets. It is every bit as good as traditional lasagne if you remember this simple trick – dip each sheet of lasagne into hot water just before you use it. This softens the pasta, making it tastier and easier to use.

A 250g/10oz packet is about the right number of sheets for this recipe.

When these three elements are all prepared, you are ready to assemble the final dish. Take a large, ovenproof casserole (preferably with lid) and rub round with a little cooking oil to prevent sticking. Place a couple of sheets of pasta on the bottom of the dish and cover with one or two tablespoons of the bolognaise sauce followed by the same amount of cheese sauce. Then add two or three more sheets of pasta and continue to layer with bolognaise and cheese sauces until the casserole dish is filled or you run out of ingredients. Sprinkle with a little grated cheese and garnish with a few slices of tomato (optional). Bake in a moderate oven for about 1 hour.

Lasagne is best served with a crunchy side-salad. Iceberg lettuce is the best, topped with slices of cucumber and tomato. A little oil-and-vinegar dressing adds the final touch.

QUICK TIP

Lasagne eaten straight from the oven can often be rather sloppy. It is FAR nicer if you cook it the day before and allow it to stand for 24 hours. The texture becomes much more solid and the pasta absorbs the flavour of the sauces, making a truly delicious taste.

One final word – don't be like Garfield and eat all this dish yourself. It's supposed to serve between four and six people. Otherwise you, too, could end up looking like this:

GARFIELD
GARFIELD
SPLUT
DON'T YOU DARE LAUGH. I HATE IT WHEN SOMEONE HAS A LAUGH AT MY EXPENSE
JIM DAVIS
© 1982 United Feature Syndicate, Inc.
SPLAT
IF I LAUGH, GARFIELD WILL KILL ME. IF I DON'T LAUGH, I'LL BURST
WAH HA HA HA!
HA HA HA, WHEEE

AWK!
JIM DAVIS
I LOVE CHASING BIRDS
© 1984 United Feature Syndicate, Inc.
EXCEPT WHEN THEY DO THAT
BOING!
RATS!
JIM DAVIS
DOUBLE RATS!
© 1984 United Feature Syndicate, Inc
AND, OF COURSE, TRIPLE RATS
SHOO!
GARFIELD
JIM DAVIS
FLIES AND I HAVE A LOT IN COMMON...
GARFIELD
© 1984 United Feature Syndicate, Inc.
YOU CAN'T KEEP EITHER OF US AWAY FROM FOOD
GARFIELD
I GOTTA BEAT THAT FLY TO MY FOOD!
JIM DAVIS
I WIN!
YOU LOSE, FELLA
PTUI
GARFIELD
© 1984 United Feature Syndicate, Inc.

WORLD-WIDE PHENOMENON

Many Garfield fans know everything there is to know about their hero. His friends, his habits, his likes and dislikes are all as familiar to them as their own. What is less well-documented, however, is the extent to which Garfield is known and loved around the world. So here are some facts about Garfield's global popularity.

NEWSPAPER TYCOON

Since the Garfield comic strip first appeared in 40 American newspapers in June, 1978, the fat cat shot to the top and is now published in more than 19 languages and 62 countries including Brazil, Venezuela, Austria, Denmark, Finland, France, Germany, Greece, Norway, the Netherlands, the United Kingdom, Iceland, Spain, Sweden, Saudi Arabia, Yugoslavia, Hong Kong, India, the Philippines, Australia, Fiji, Mexico and El Salvador! In only 10 years, Garfield became only the second comic strip in history to appear in more than 2,100 newspapers around the world.

TV SUPERSTAR

Having taken the newspaper and book-publishing worlds by storm, it was only natural that the feline superstar should find his way onto television. In 1982, he made a spectacular debut on American Network television with an animated adventure called 'Here Comes Garfield'. More adventures have followed and there are now eight Garfield television specials shown in 45 countries worldwide. Furthermore, a series of 21 half-hour animated shows, called 'Garfield and Friends', have been shown on Saturday mornings in America and are now available for screening elsewhere.

BOOK BARON

Garfield's runaway success in the newspapers soon led to his appearance in book form. The first Garfield book came out in 1980 and was called 'Garfield at Large'. Since then, Garfield books have been published in 23 countries and 17 different languages and have sold in their millions. In addition to this there is GARFIELD, a monthly magazine published in eight languages and sold throughout Europe. (Not to mention the 'Birthday Special', a one-off magazine published in seven languages to celebrate Garfield's 10th birthday, which proved to be another best-seller.)

Why GARFIELD?

Why has Garfield achieved this phenomenal worldwide success? His creator, Jim Davis, explains: "With Garfield, I was trying to make everybody laugh. Everybody. In Sweden, they call him Gustaf. In Norway, it's Pusur. In Denmark, he's Karvinen, but the gags are always the same. Garfield is out there as our champion, saying, "Go ahead! Have dessert! Sleep late! Who needs to exercise?"

Why is Garfield called Garfield? Jim Davis named his wonderful, funny, loveable character after his grandfather, James A. Garfield Davies.

THE KNIGHT BEFORE CHRISTMAS

Garfield was feeling very miserable. He had fallen out with Arlene – again! "What did you do this time?" asked Nermal, who had come round for a visit. "Nothing!" replied Garfield. "Oh, come on," insisted the kitten, "you must have done something to upset her." "I just told the truth." sighed Garfield, wearily.

The previous day, Garfield had a date with Arlene. They were just leaving when Jon placed a pan of freshly-baked lasagne on the floor in front of his cat. "You'll have to choose between that lasagne and me!" snapped Arlene."No contest!" grinned Garfield, picking up the pan. So Arlene left in a huff."And I haven't seen her since," concluded the lovesick pussy. "Poor old Garfield," chuckled Nermal, skipping out of the door, "I'm glad I'm too young for affairs of the heart. 'Bye, now!"

Then Garfield heard the postman in the drive. He felt too fed-up to bother attacking him, so the letter just plopped onto the mat. "Let it stay there," thought Garfield. Suddenly, though, he remembered that it was Christmas Eve and Arlene was holding a fancy dress party that evening. "This will be my invitation!" whooped Garfield, rushing to the door. "Arlene wants to make up with me."

The invitation was addressed to Odie! There was nothing for Garfield. "Go into the playroom and choose an outfit from our box of dressing-up clothes," Garfield told the excited puppy. Odie bounded away and returned a few minutes later, dressed as The Easter Bunny. "It's Christmas, Odie," groaned Garfield, "you **are** a dope!"

Garfield found another outfit for Odie who scampered away, holding his invitation in his mouth. Garfield thumbed idly through the other costumes in the box. "Bet I'd look really good in one of these," he sighed.

KING TUTANGARFIELD

JULIUS GARFIELD

ROBIN GARFIELD

Then Garfield had an idea. "I **will** go to Arlene's party!" exclaimed Garfield. "When she sees me in my fancy dress, I'll look so handsome that her heart will melt and she will invite me in." So Garfield began trying on the outfits. He could not make up his mind which one suited him best.

WILD BILL GARFIELD

SIR ISAAC GARFIELD

LONG JOHN GARFIELD

In the end, Garfield decided on none of those costumes. "I shall dress up as a knight of old!" he exclaimed, clambering into a suit of toy armour. "Behold Sir Garfield of the Round Pizza!"

Early that evening, Garfield set off for the party. "I'll be the first there," he thought, "then Arlene and I will have a few moments alone together." As he clumped along through the snow-covered streets, Garfield began to feel like a real old-fashioned knight. He pretended that Arlene's house was a castle and a little tree in front of it was a fierce giant. Garfield fought the ogre – and won! "I just hope I don't meet any fire-breathing dragons," thought Garfield, "this plastic armour is likely to melt!"

Garfield had not gone much further when he heard cries for help. "Egad!" he exclaimed in his best knightly voice, "A damsel in distress!" Looking up, Garfield saw another cat clinging precariously to the roof of the house. "It's Arlene!" gasped Garfield. "The damsel in distress is Arlene!"

Garfield ran forwards to help. "Go away!" shouted Arlene, "I'm not speaking to you." "Don't be silly, "replied Garfield, "you're about to fall off the roof." Arlene had gone to the attic of her house to find a fancy dress outfit for her party. While she was up there, the door had blown shut and Arlene found herself trapped, so she had tried to climb out of the window. "Go back inside," yelled Garfield, "I'll rescue you!"

Brave Sir Garfield raced in through the front door and clattered up the stairs to the attic. A single blow from his trusty toy sword and the attic door swung open. Arlene was free. "My hero!" she swooned.

Arlene had intended to go to her party as Florence Arlene, the cat with the lamp. "I won't wear my nurse's outfit now," she told Garfield, "I'll dress up as a beautiful old-fashioned lady and go with you."

Odie and the other guests had already arrived downstairs as Garfield and Arlene came down from the attic. "Meet bold Sir Garfield and his Queen," announced Garfield, holding his sword aloft. "Steady on, Garfield," whispered Arlene. "Don't overdo it!"

Garfield turned to his girlfriend. "You're a Queen to me," he said, simply. Arlene's face broke out into a big, beaming smile. "I especially love that gap in your teeth!" added Garfield.

Arlene's Christmas Eve party was the best party that Garfield had ever attended. (And he's been to quite a few in his time!) Afterwards, Garfield helped to clear up by polishing-off all the left-over food. Then the happy couple said goodnight on the porch. "This is going to be my happiest Christmas ever," chuckled Garfield.

STAR PORTRAIT
ODIE

GARFIELD
LET'S SEE, IT'S OVER AND UNDER, THEN THROUGH
I'M TAKING YOU OUT TO EAT, GARFIELD. YOU'LL HAVE TO WEAR THIS TO GET INTO THE RESTAURANT
© 1985 United Feature Syndicate,Inc
I'LL HAVE A STEAK AND MY CA...ER... SON HERE WILL HAVE A TRIPLE ORDER OF LASAGNA AND A CUP OF COCOA
Vince's
THIS IS AN EXCLUSIVE RESTAURANT, GARFIELD. USE YOUR SILVERWARE
GULP! SLURP! GULP!
JIM DAVIS
THAT MARSHMALLOW IS MEANT FOR YOUR COCOA
HEH, HEH. DON'T LICK YOUR PAWS AT THE TABLE, SON
THAT'S THE RUDEST LITTLE KID I'VE EVER SEEN!
HE EVEN SHED ON THE TABLECLOTH

HI, THIS IS JON ARBUCKLE. MY CAT NEEDS A CHECKUP... WHAT KIND OF CAT IS HE?
UH, HE'S A REGISTERED YELLOW TABBY WITH DISTINGUISHED LINEAGE
ACTUALLY, HE'S AN ORANGE MEATBALL WITH STRIPES
© 1986 United Feature Syndicate, Inc.
JIM DAVIS
THE DOCTOR'S NOT LOOKING. NOW'S MY CHANCE TO MAKE AN ESCAPE!
JIM DAVIS
© 1986 United Feature Syndicate, Inc.
STUPID STAINLESS STEEL TABLE
HEY, DOC, DO YOU MIND IF I HAVE SOMETHING TO DRINK?
JIM DAVIS
HELP YOURSELF
© 1986 United Feature Syndicate, Inc
THERE SHOULD BE SOMETHING IN THE REFRIGERATOR BY THE SPECIMEN BOTTLES
WHILE YOU'RE AT IT, DOC, HOW ABOUT GIVING ME A CHECKUP?
SAY "AHH"
JIM DAVIS 2-8
AHH
WHAT WAS THAT?!
YOU'LL NEVER HAVE TO WORRY ABOUT LIVER FLUKES AGAIN
© 1986 United Feature Syndicate, Inc.

SURPRISE! I GOT YOU A CANOPY BED!
ALL RIGHT!
I FEEL LIKE A SISSY
© 1985 United Feature Syndicate, Inc.
JIM DAVIS
YAWN
WHA?!
THESE CANOPY BEDS TAKE SOME GETTING USED TO
© 1985 United Feature Syndicate, Inc.
JIM DAVIS
ARE YOU ASHAMED OF YOUR NEW BED, GARFIELD?
WHAT GIVES YOU THAT IDEA?
© 1985 United Feature Syndicate, Inc.
JIM DAVIS
JON FINALLY GOT ME A BED WITH SOME CLASS
BUT IT'S JUST NOT ME. I HAVE MY PRIDE
AND PRIDE, OF COURSE, IS THE MIDDLE CLASS SUBSTITUTE FOR CLASS
© 1985 United Feature Syndicate, Inc.
JIM DAVIS

MORNIN', HON
MORNIN', IRMA
JIM DAVIS
SAY WHEN
© 1985 United Feature Syndicate, Inc.
WHEN
THESE PEOPLE NEED HELP
HEY! WHERE'S THE WAITRESS IN THIS CRUMMY DIVE?! THE SERVICE HERE STINKS!
WHO'S THE MANAGER HERE ANYWAY?!
YOU ARE
© 1985 United Feature Syndicate, Inc.
SMACK!
FORGOT
I'M GOING HOME
SMACK!
JIM DAVIS
JIM DAVIS
I DON'T SEE HOW YOU DO IT, IRMA
HOW DO YOU KEEP THIS PLACE OPEN 24 HOURS WITH NO HELP?
© 1985 United Feature Syndicate, Inc.
NOW I SEE HOW SHE DOES IT
SHEER WILL-POWER
Z
HERE'S YOUR EGG, HON. WHATEVER YOU DO, TRY NOT TO THINK ABOUT WHERE IT CAME FROM
© 1985 United Feature Syndicate, Inc.
HAVE AN EGG, GARFIELD
TOO LATE. I ALREADY THOUGHT ABOUT IT
JIM DAVIS

QUICK CROSSWORD

Hi, readers. Did you know I'm an expert at crosswords? I'm always having them with Jon, Odie and Arlene! Ha, Ha! Just my little joke!

Actually, I've penned a puzzle for you to solve. The clues are nice and easy, so you should be able to finish in the time it takes me to eat a lasagne. Not possible? Well, see how close you can get. The solution is printed upside-down at the bottom of the page.

Across:

1. I, me, myself! (8)
6. You find this in the fridge. (3)
7. Proper name for a family of kittens. (6)
9. I was this in 1988 (special birthday). (3)
10. Many little cats are called this. (5)
13. Where I sleep. (3)
15. The insect that I can't stand! (6)
16. Liz's job. (3)
17. I have never been this! (4)
18. Places where you go out of a building. (5)

Down:

1. Jon wears funny clothes when dressed for this game. (4)
2. I have ALWAYS been this! (3)
3. I hate getting up at this time. (5)
4. I'm always on one to lose weight. (4)
5. My favourite houseplant. (4)
8. A long, cool drink solves this problem. (6)
11. Odie is always wagging this. (4)
12. American word for a cinema film. (5)
13. I don't reckon Odie has one of these! (5)
14. Odie IS one of these! (3)

NOW CHECK YOUR ANSWERS

Solution:

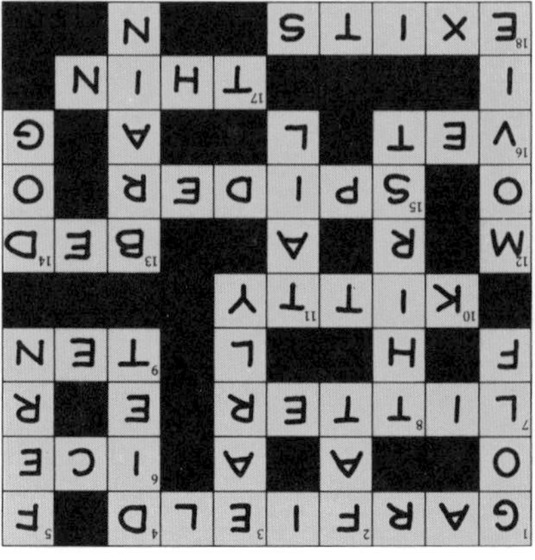

STAR PORTRAIT
NERMAL

NERMAL'S Kitten Corner

Hi, everyone! It's me, the world's cutest kitten!

Now I know that many of you will be getting a kitten of your own this Christmas. So here are a few 'handy hints' to help you look after the loveable little rascal.

We cats spend a lot of time asleep, so we need a warm, dry, comfortable bed. If you can't afford a proper cat basket, a cardboard box makes an excellent bed. It can be lined with newspaper which is cosy, cheap and easily changed.

Kittens are naturally very clean creatures, so house-training us shouldn't be much of a problem. All we ask is a leak-proof litter tray placed in a quiet corner and filled with sand, dry earth or specially bought cat litter. Remember, when you wash out the tray, don't use bleach or disinfectant containing carbolic acid because that makes us ill.

We all know how much my friend, Garfield, loves his food. The same is true of us kittens. We have mammoth appetites. Up until the age of 12 weeks, we should have 4 small meals a day, spaced out at regular intervals. We like fresh fish, finely-chopped meat or tinned food specially made for kittens. Please don't give us the crunchy type of cat food until we are older.

When you first bring your kitten home, remember that it will seem very strange to him. It is probably better to confine him to a single room to start with and let him explore the rest of the house when he has settled down. Feed him, give him a litter tray, play with him and give him lots of love, then leave him to sleep in peace. Don't let him out until you are sure he won't run off.

You must remember to take your kitten to the vet around the age of 12 weeks. It's very important that we have our injection against cat 'flu and feline enteritis. Both diseases can kill the healthiest kitten. Also, ask your vet about worms. Most kittens are born with roundworm, but this common complaint is easily treated.

Kittens like me are full of energy. We need things to play with. These can be proper toys from the pet shop or just a piece of string or screwed-up paper. My favourite is an old ping-pong ball which I chase round the room. (I'm a better dribbler than Bryan Robson!) If you don't want me to scratch the furniture, how about providing a scratching-post for sharpening my claws?

Well, that's all I have room for, I'm afraid. I'm off to visit Garfield now. He was a kitten once. As I keep reminding him – it was MANY years ago! 'Bye!

Information kindly provided by the RSPCA.
For detailed booklet, 'Cats and Kittens', write to:
RSPCA, The Causeway, Horsham, West Sussex RH12 1HG.

GARFIELD
© 1982 United Feature Syndicate, Inc.
JIM DAVIS
HOW ABOUT A SHOT OF FLEA POWDER, GARFIELD?
IF YOU CAN HIT A MOVING TARGET
SCHHREEEK
GARFIELD
I GUESS IT'S SAFE TO EAT
GARFIELD
GOTCHA!
I GUESS I PULLED A GOOD ONE ON GARFIELD
GUESS AGAIN, SUCKER

HEY, JUDY! HOW ARE YOU, CUZ? YEAH, WE'LL BE HOME. COME ON OVER
SURE, BRING THE KIDS, TOO
© 1985 United Feature Syndicate, Inc.
JIM DAVIS
GARFIELD?
TIERRA DEL FUEGO
MY COUSIN JUDY IS COMING TO VISIT AND SHE'S BRINGING HER CHILDREN
SO PUT EVERYTHING YOU VALUE OUT OF REACH
© 1985 United Feature Syndicate, Inc.
JIM DAVIS
GARFIELD, THIS IS MY COUSIN JUDY AND HER CHILDREN, TAMMY AND STEVIE
JIM DAVIS
BALL! BALL!
© 1985 United Feature Syndicate, Inc.
OH, LISTEN! STEVIE'S FIRST WORDS!
AND HIS LAST
DO YOU KNOW WHY I DON'T LIKE KIDS?
JIM DAVIS
I'LL GIVE YOU THREE GUESSES
© 1985 United Feature Syndicate, Inc.
...AND THE FIRST TWO DON'T COUNT

Christmas is a T

ne for Reflection

COME BACK, POOKY

I Miss You!

Poor old Garfield! He has lost Pooky! The fat cat's special teddy is stuck in the middle of a maze. Can you show Garfield how to reach him?

STAR PORTRAIT
ARLENE

GARFIELD
GOOD MORNING, SUNSHINE
POKE POKE POKE

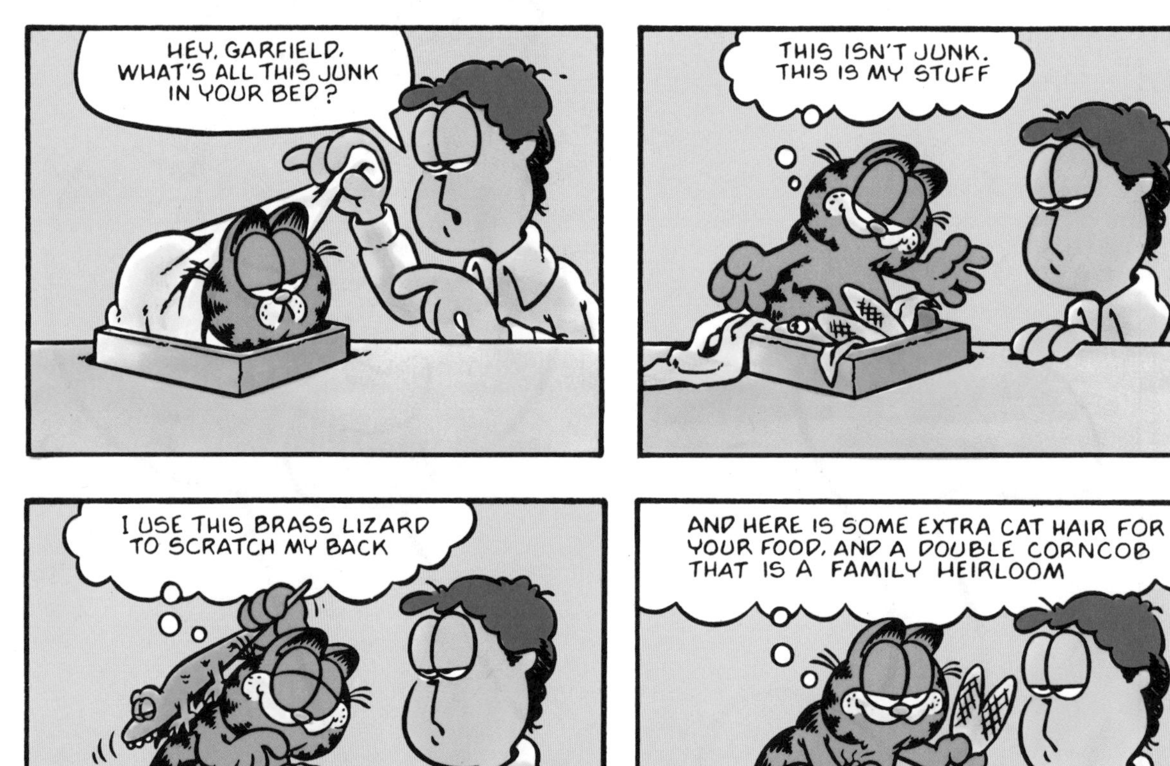
HEY, GARFIELD, WHAT'S ALL THIS JUNK IN YOUR BED?
THIS ISN'T JUNK. THIS IS MY STUFF
I USE THIS BRASS LIZARD TO SCRATCH MY BACK
AND HERE IS SOME EXTRA CAT HAIR FOR YOUR FOOD, AND A DOUBLE CORNCOB THAT IS A FAMILY HEIRLOOM

AND THIS IS MY BEAN-FILLED WHACK-BONK
WHAT DOES THAT DO?
© 1984 United Feature Syndicate, Inc.

WHACK!
BONK
JIM DAVIS

GARFIELD, I THINK YOU'RE TOO MEAN TO ODIE
JIM DAVIS
I NEVER WANT TO SEE YOU HIT HIM AGAIN
OH, VERY WELL
© 1984 United Feature Syndicate, Inc.
KONK!
I'M GOING TO THE STORE, GARFIELD. IF YOU LAY A PAW ON ODIE, I'LL SPANK YOU
© 1984 United Feature Syndicate, Inc.
BOING
JIM DAVIS
GARFIELD, I SWEAR YOU'VE DONE EVERYTHING TO ODIE A CAT COULD DO TO A DOG
AU CONTRAIRE
JIM DAVIS
© 1984 United Feature Syndicate, Inc.
PLINK
NEVER UNDERESTIMATE ME
HEY, ODIE! I FOUND YOUR NOSE!
LET ME PUT IT ON FOR YOU, PAL
SQUIK SQUIK
© 1984 United Feature Syndicate, Inc.
VERY NICE. I LIKE YOU AS A RAT TERRIER
SNIFF
JIM DAVIS

I LOVE YOUR PURR, GARFIELD
PURRR
I WISH THERE WERE A WAY TO GET THE PURR WITHOUT THE CAT
PURRR
BUT I GUESS YOU HAVE TO TAKE THE BAD WITH THE GOOD
YOU'RE TREADING ON THIN ICE, FELLA
© 1984 United Feature Syndicate,Inc.
JIM DAVIS
READY FOR A GOURMET MEAL, GARFIELD?
WHAM!
I HATE SPIDERS
JIM DAVIS
© 1984 United Feature Syndicate,Inc.
ONE NICE THING ABOUT CONFIDING IN PETS IS THAT THEY ARE NON-JUDG-MENTAL
GARFIELD, I GOT A SPEEDING TICKET TODAY
THAT WAS A STUPID THING TO DO
SMACK!
JIM DAVIS
© 1984 United Feature Syndicate,Inc.
WHY, THANK YOU, GARFIELD!
COLA
PSHHH
JIM DAVIS
© 1984 United Feature Syndicate,Inc.

HEY, GARFIELD! ARE YOU READY TO GO PLAY GOLF?
© 1984 United Feature Syndicate, Inc.
JIM DAVIS
AREN'T YOU COMING?
ON SECOND THOUGHT, I THINK I'D RATHER STAY IN THE ROOM AND WATCH THE SINK BACK-UP
ODIE! GET AWAY FROM THAT TREE! GARFIELD! GET OUT OF THAT SAND TRAP!
JIM DAVIS
WOULD YOU MIND OBSERVING PROPER GOLF ETIQUETTE THERE, MISTER?
© 1984 United Feature Syndicate, Inc.
I'M SORRY, BUT MY PETS ARE DRIVING ME NUTS
IT'S THE OUTFIT I'M TALKING ABOUT
CRACK!
JIM DAVIS
OH, NO! I HIT AN OLD LADY IN THE HEAD AND KNOCKED HER OUT COLD!
© 1984 United Feature Syndicate, Inc.
WHAT SHOULD I DO, GARFIELD?!
I'D STRAIGHTEN THAT LEFT ARM A BIT AND TURN THAT RIGHT HAND OVER MORE
JIM DAVIS
© 1984 United Feature Syndicate, Inc.
ROWR!
GARFIELD! WHAT ARE YOU DOING IN THAT SAND TRAP?
SQUATTING ON A SANDBUR, THANK YOU

COLOUR ME

Here is a picture of Garfield, Pooky, Odie, Nermal and Arlene playing 'hide-and-seek' in the garden. You can colour the picture with felt-tips, paints or crayons.

Garfield THE EAGLE

Jon had a date. "I've invited Miriam round for lunch, Garfield," called Jon. "Aren't you pleased for me?" "Not as pleased as I am for myself," thought Garfield, with a sly chuckle. "A lunch-date for Jon means food – lots and lots of yummy food!"

Sure enough, Jon hurried off to the supermarket and returned with a basket full of delicious goodies. He laid everything out on the dining-room table. "Now don't you go sneaking in there while my back's turned," warned Jon. "As if I would," chuckled Garfield. "I'll sneak in there right under your very nose!"

DING-DONG went the doorbell. "Come in, Miriam!" beamed Jon. Garfield waited until Jon was busy chatting to his would-be girlfriend, then he made his move. "Snack attack!" he sniggered.

Garfield ate everything on the table. Then he closed his eyes. "I feel sleepy now," he yawned. The next thing Garfield heard was his name being bellowed in his ear! "You've ruined my date!" yelled Jon. "Miriam's gone home now!" "S-S-Sorry!" hiccupped Garfield. "That's not good enough!" roared Jon, "I'm putting you on a strict diet! You've got to learn to control that appetite of yours!"

Garfield slouched into the sitting-room and flopped down on the sofa. "Life isn't going to be worth living from now on," he groaned. Garfield imagined himself nibbling a lettuce-leaf day after day. "If only I could lose weight quickly," thought Garfield, "Jon would change his mind and start feeding me again."

The only way to lose weight was exercise, but Garfield disliked that nearly as much as dieting! Then the fat cat remembered seeing Eddie the Eagle, the British ski-jumping champion, at the Winter Olympics. "Skiing's good exercise," exclaimed Garfield, "but it doesn't look too energetic. You just have to stand on the skis and slide along. I'll try it!"

There was plenty of snow outside. And Jon kept an old set of skis and some goggles in the garage. Garfield borrowed them and set off.

"Hey! This is easy!" giggled Garfield.

"Er . . . maybe it's not quite as easy as it looks!"

"Oooer! My left leg won't do anything I tell it to!"

"Help! we have lift-off!"

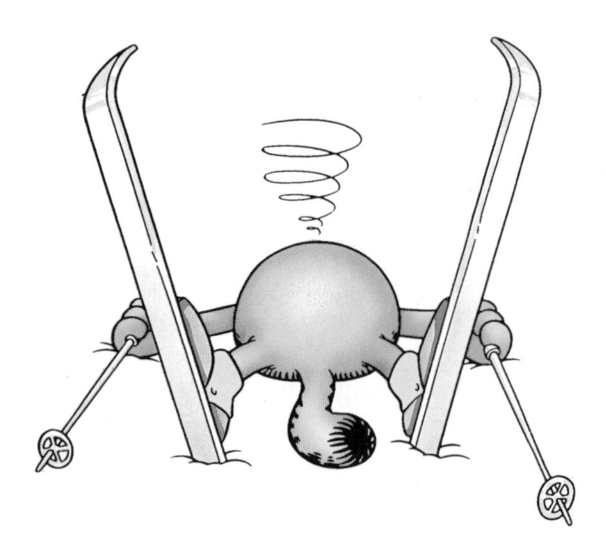

"The skiing's all right. It's the falling down that gets you!"

"I'm not going to be beaten by these stupid skis!"

"Hey! I've got the hang of it now!"

"Look, Mum. No hands!"

"Sorry, Eddie – you're an EX-champion!"

"I can even do jumps!"

"WOW! Look where I've landed! Garfield the Eagle is ready to fly now!"

Meanwhile, back at home, Jon had gone for a lie-down. All that shouting at Garfield had given him a headache. He was just drifting off to sleep, dreaming of a romantic date, when there was a tremendous CRASH outside the window. Jon sat up with a start. "What on earth was that?" he gasped.

Jon hurried outside. He found Garfield stuck head-first in the wall! "What happened, old fella?" he cried. "Oh, nothing," groaned Garfield, "I just need to work on my landings. Now get me out of here."

Jon rescued his cat and put him to bed with Pooky. "Now you stay there for the next few days," ordered Jon. Garfield did not argue. He felt too shaken-up. "That crash has even knocked the appetite out of me," he told his teddy.

Before very long, Garfield was up and about again. Jon also had some news for him. "I'm glad you spoiled my lunch-date the other day," he said, "that girl Miriam has a boyfriend who's a twenty-stone rugby player. If he had found out, I would have been pulped!"

Garfield stopped dead in his tracks. "Does that mean I'm forgiven?" he wondered. "I've decided to forgive you," announced Jon. "And does that mean I don't have to stay on a diet? " thought Garfield. "So I'm going to take off your diet," added Jon. "Whoopee!" shrieked Garfield, rushing to the nearest open tin. "FOOD!"

The best was yet to come. Jon had bought Miriam a box of chocolates. "I certainly won't be giving them to her now," said Jon, "so you might as well have them."

Garfield settled back on a cushion and tucked into the chocolates. "Being Garfield the Eagle was fun," he thought, "but I'd much rather be Garfield the Gannet!"